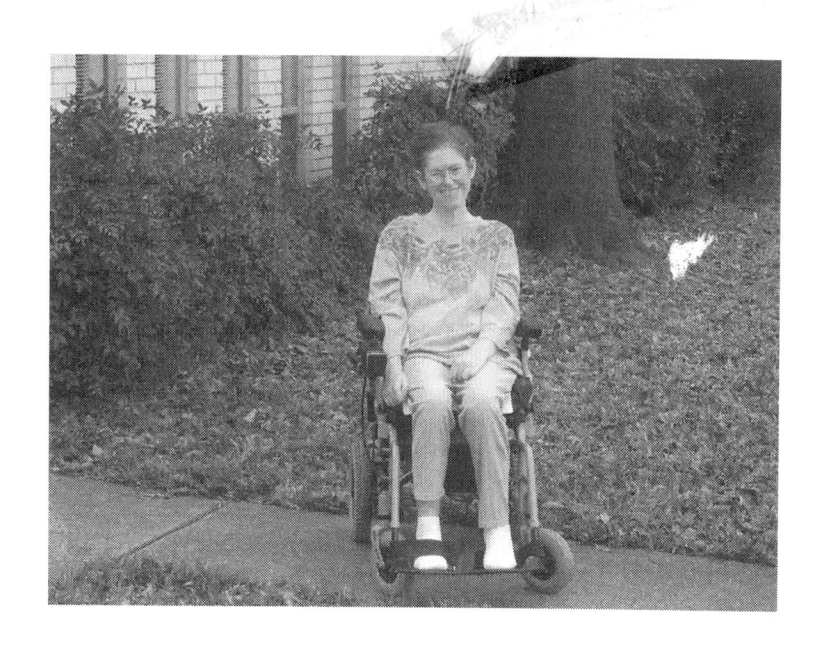

MY BATTLE

WITH

PRIMARY LATERAL SCLEROSIS:

A Story of Survival, Strength, and the Will to Stand

Again

By Beth Geiger

(1953-2008)

PLS can cause severe spasticity and weakness in the muscles of the upper and lower extremities, throat and neck. Neither PLS nor ALS affect the mind. There is no known cause for most cases of PLS or ALS. To-date there is no cure for PLS or ALS.

My name is Beth. (I am 48 years old). I have primary lateral sclerosis (PLS). PLS is a little known variation of amyotrophic lateral sclerosis (ALS), also called Lou Gehrig's disease. Like ALS, PLS affects each person differently. ALS usually progresses rapidly. It can become life threatening within a few years. PLS is generally not life threatening. It usually progresses slowly over several years.

PLS is hard to diagnose because there is not a definitive test for it. I showed my first symptoms about 25 years ago. I was referred to a neurologist in 1980. I did not hear the words primary lateral sclerosis until 1987, at which time I was diagnosed with probable PLS. I did not get a definitive diagnosis of PLS until 1989.

About 10% of PLS is hereditary. There is no prior history of PLS in my family. However, my brother (who is two years younger than me) started showing PLS symptoms about 10 years ago. Neither of my sisters have shown any PLS symptoms. I worry about my daughters (who are 20 & 21) getting PLS.

To look at me you wouldn't think I could do anything. PLS has affected my legs, arms, hands, throat, neck and tongue. It has left me totally physically disabled. I am confined to a wheelchair. PLS has robbed me of the ability to do anything for myself. I require around-the-clock care. I need assistance in all activities of daily living: eating, bathing, dressing, toileting, brushing my teeth & hair, and getting into & out of my wheelchair and my bed.

PLS has left me unable to swallow liquids. I had to have a feeding tube put in my stomach to prevent dehydration. I am still able to swallow soft food and pureed food.

PLS has left my speech unintelligible. I communicate by writing letters. I type by pressing one key at a time on a computer keyboard with the end of a pen, which is strapped to my right hand. I put my right arm in a sling to hold it up. It takes me about 3 hours to type a one-page letter.

I would like to share the story of my battle with primary lateral sclerosis, beginning a couple of years before I started showing PLS symptoms. By sharing my story, I hope to help other people with problems similar to mine.

(Note: To protect my daughters I have not used their names or my husband's name in my story)

I graduated from Westchester High School, in Houston, in May 1971. I went to Southwest Texas State University, in San Marcos. (San Marcos is between Austin and San Antonio). In July 1972, after my first year of college, I met a guy (a year older than me) who I thought was my "Prince Charming." The YMCA, in west Houston, offered a 2 week (day) camp for children with special needs. I was a volunteer counselor for the children. He worked for the YMCA. (He graduated from Spring Branch High School in May 1971. Spring Branch was about 5 miles from Westchester). He "wined and dined" me. He made me feel special. We became engaged during my second year of college.

We were married in Houston (where both of our parents' lived), in September 1973. Much to my parents' dismay, I quit college and moved to San Antonio, where my husband was stationed. He was a Security Policeman in the Air Force.

In June 1974, my husband was electrocuted when an antenna he was trying to install on the roof of our mobile home hit the power lines. I watched in horror while electricity attacked his body. His hands and feet looked like they were on fire. (This image is still vivid in my mind). I felt totally helpless. There was not anything I could do to help him. I was certain I was witnessing his death. My first thoughts were of his mother, and how I could possibly tell her that her (only) son was dead. Her husband had died less than 4 months earlier.

After what seemed like an eternity (but was probably less than 3 minutes), my husband's seemingly lifeless body fell to the ground. Though I knew it might be a futile effort, I immediately began mouth-to-mouth resuscitation. To my amazement, it worked! I kept it up until help arrived from neighbors who had heard me screaming. One of my husband's doctors told me that my quick, clearheaded actions may have helped save his life.

My husband was rushed to a nearby military hospital. He spent 2 months there. I spent 10-12 hours a day with my husband while he was in the hospital. His right hand had to be amputated. He was fitted with a prosthesis; he became quite adept at using his hook. It took several surgeries and grafts, done over a 2-year period, to restore limited function to his left hand.

I took care of my husband during his lengthy recuperation. I fed him, bathed him, dressed him, exercised his fingers, and helped him in any way I could. I learned how to change the oil in a car. I even installed shock absorbers on his van. I did all of this out of love for my husband, not out of duty or obligation to him.

During the time my husband recuperated he noticed that I would shiver occasionally as though I were cold. He pointed this behavior out to me each time it occurred. Though he was concerned, I was not. I felt fine. I did not want to go to a doctor just because I shivered for no apparent reason.

My husband received a medical retirement from the Air Force. We both went to The University of Texas at San Antonio. I pursued a degree in Elementary Education and certification in Special Education. My husband pursued a degree in Criminal Justice.

I graduated in December 1977. I accepted a teaching position at the Cerebral Palsy Center in San Antonio. I worked with severely physically disabled children ranging in age from 6-15. They were all in wheelchairs. Most of them could not talk. About half of them required around-the-clock care. I never thought I would need around-the-clock care.

Not all of my students were mentally impaired. Some of them had perfectly normal minds that were trapped in bodies that would not work. I never dreamed that someday I would be in this position.

My aides and I tried to establish a means of communication with each child. For the most severely involved children, we would use eye contact. For example, we would ask them a question and have them look to the right if the answer was yes, and to the left if the answer was no. (This was in the pre-computer era). I never thought I would need to use augmentative communication.

We spent much of our time doing stretching exercises on our students, under the supervision of physical and occupational therapists. I saw, firsthand, what spasticity and atrophy can do to one's body. I never thought I would need to have stretching exercises done on me.

I became familiar with many types of adaptive equipment: braces and splints, communication boards, writing and eating utensils. I also never thought that I would need to use adaptive devices.

I loved my students as much as I love my own children. They taught me a lot about unconditional love. Their radiant smiles, in the face of adversity, melted my heart. Whenever I start feeling sorry for myself or frustrated by my physical limitations, I think of my students and the physical limitations they faced (which are greater than mine), and I count my blessings. My students are an inspiration to me. Remembering them gives me courage to face my problems each day.

During the time I was teaching, my "shivers" continued. Also, I began to jump and sometimes even fall whenever a noise startled me: a doorbell, a telephone, or someone's voice behind me. My family and co-workers expressed their concerns, but I thought it was much ado about nothing.

During the summer of 1979, I became pregnant. I was thrilled! I had wanted to have a baby for several months. I expected to have a normal pregnancy. After all, thousands of women have babies every year. I had a high-risk pregnancy. My blood pressure started rising soon after I became pregnant. On the advice of my obstetrician, I quit teaching at the end of November 1979.

I rested as much as possible. My blood pressure got dangerously high in early February 1980 and I was hospitalized. My first daughter was born, by C-section, in early March 1980. My daughter was healthy, but I developed post-operative problems. It took me about 4 months to fully recover from them.

During the last 2 months of my pregnancy, my obstetrician expressed concern about my reflexes. He attributed this to the pre-eclampsia that I had developed. When my reflexes were still "hyper" 2 months after I had my daughter, I was referred to a neurologist. She put me in the hospital for 5 days "for tests. In May 1980, I underwent my first round of tests. I had a complete lab work-up, an EKG, an EEG, a spinal tap, and a CT scan. All of the test results were normal.

I was told that I might be in the beginning stages of multiple sclerosis (MS), but that it was more likely that my problems were caused by the mumps meningitis that I had in 1960, at age 7. I was told to see my internist in a year.

In the fall of 1980, I became pregnant again. I had problems with my blood pressure, but not as severe. My second daughter had problems with her heart rate and was delivered by emergency C-section in late May 1981. She was born a few weeks early. She quit breathing shortly after she was born. She had to spend several days in Neo-Natal ICU. I didn't have any post-operative problems.

I had a checkup with my internist in June 1981. He found no new problems. He told me to see a neurologist immediately if my problems worsened or if I developed any new problems.

In July 1981, my husband accepted a job in the

Houston area. We bought a house in Pearland (a town about 15 miles south of Houston). I was too busy taking care of 2 babies and my husband to worry about my own health. For months, I never got more than 4-5 hours of sleep a day, in 2-3 hour increments. My health suffered and my problems started to get worse. I began to have great difficulty walking. My hips would become so painful when I was walking, that my legs would buckle and I would fall. I could not step down off a curb. I began to lose strength in my hands. I could not hold on to heavy pans. I could not hold up 3 fingers.

In the fall of 1983, my Mom convinced me to see a neurologist. (Because my husband was medically retired from the Air Force, we had free medical coverage at two facilities in the Houston area). I got a referral to see a neurologist, about 15 miles from our house. She put me in the hospital for tests.

In December 1983, I underwent my second round of tests. I had a complete lab work-up, an EKG, an EEG, a spinal tap, and a CT scan. All of the test results were normal. The neurologist felt that I may have multiple sclerosis or that I may be suffering from the after- effects of mumps meningitis.

I saw the neurologist every few months. She put me on an anti-inflammatory because of my hip pain. In 1984, she prescribed physical therapy, which she hoped would help my problems. I went to physical therapy 2-3 times a week. I worked out on a couple of machines for strengthening. My therapist did a complete range-of-motion program for my arms and legs. My therapist also worked on gait training}with me, but I couldn't quit "toe-walking." My therapist thought that I walked on the balls of my feet because my heel cords were so tight.

I kept getting worse. The neurologist could not understand why. I think this really frustrated her. In late 1984, she told me not to come back to her again because there was nothing more she could do for me.

I was shocked! I began to wonder if there really was something medically wrong with me. My Mom talked me into seeing a different neurologist. He was a warm, caring person who seemed to be genuinely interested in my case.

He said he didn't know what was wrong with me. He added to the list of theories as to what was causing my problems: the after-effects of mumps meningitis, the after-effects of pre- eclampsia that I developed during both of my pregnancies, being overweight (I used to weigh nearly 200 pounds, I now weigh about 140) and too much stress (I have always thought that stress was a significant factor in my case). He said he hoped that my condition would improve with medication

(Baclofen) and physical therapy. I saw him once a month.

In early 1987, when a 25mph wind literally blew me down, my therapist gave me a walker. My therapist tried to teach me how to walk with the walker. However, I only used my walker to go to and from therapy, and when it was windy. Most of the time I "toe-walked" because it was faster.

Despite taking Baclofen daily and receiving physical therapy 2-3 times a week, I continued to slowly and steadily get worse. No one could tell me why. I became more and more frustrated. At times, I thought that I was losing my mind. My husband contended that my only problems were that I was fat and lazy.

In September 1986, my husband accepted a job in a small community in North East Texas. My daughters and I stayed in our house in Pearland until we sold it. My husband came home almost every weekend.

In April 1987, we moved into a beautiful house, which overlooked a lake, in Sulphur Springs (a small town in North East Texas, between Dallas and Texarkana). I was too busy getting settled into a new home and in a new community to worry about my health problems. I had a prescription for a 3-month supply of Baclofen and the anti-inflammatory I was taking.

(Between 1985 & 1987, I had undergone more tests: lab work-ups, CT Scans, EEGs, and MRIs. The test results were all normal). In July 1987, my daughters and I came to Houston to visit my parents. I went to see my neurologist in Houston. He decided to run more tests. Again, all the results were normal.

My neurologist was fairly certain I did not have multiple sclerosis, but I probably had primary lateral sclerosis. He was not 100% sure since there was not a definitive test for PLS. He told me that PLS was progressive, that Baclofen and physical therapy would hopefully help slow the progression, but nothing could stop it. He told me that he did not know much about PLS. I was the first case he'd seen in his 20+ years of practice. (Most doctors, including many neurologists, never see a case of PLS).

After 7 years, I was greatly relieved to learn a name for what was "probably" wrong with me. I immediately tried to find out everything I could about PLS. I soon became frustrated at how little information there is on PLS. One doctor told me little research has been done on PLS because it affects so few people.

My neurologist had given me a prescription for a 4-month supply of my medications. He told me to find a neurologist in North East Texas to treat me. I put off going to a doctor since we no longer had access to free medical care. The closest government medical facility was about 90 miles from our house. We had to pay for our medical care and file for reimbursement. We had 75% insurance coverage through a government program (CHAMPUS). We bought a supplemental policy which, after a year, covered the other 25%.

I ran out of my medications in November. I went to see a family practice physician in Sulphur Springs. He was a very caring person. He arranged for me to get physical therapy 2-3 times a week, at a facility in Sulphur Springs. He found a neurologist who he felt would best suit my needs. Her office was about 40 miles from our house. I saw her every few months. She had seen one case of PLS when she was in medical school.

For optimal benefit, I needed range-of-motion exercises every day. My therapist showed my husband how to do them. My husband assured the therapist he would do them. He rarely did them, though.

My husband could not accept my PLS. I was a source of embarrassment to him. He was frequently verbally abusive, especially to me. He considered me "the most useless, worthless creature on the face of the earth" and he treated me accordingly. This really hurt me! I was there for my husband after his accident. I never once put him down. I constantly assured him that he was still a worthy human being, and that the loss of his hand did not change my love for him.

My doctors prescribed adaptive equipment for me, which they hoped would make my life easier. Most of these prescriptions went unfilled. My husband was not going to spend "his hard earned money on junk that I probably wouldn't use." The only thing my husband allowed me to have was a pair of arm supports for the toilet. He wouldn't let me get a raised toilet seat, so it took me up to 20 minutes to stand up. He refused to put a grab bar in the shower, even though I had fallen in the shower before. He did not want to install anything permanent in our house because he felt that would detract from the value of our house and we would have a hard time selling it.

By 1988 I used my walker anytime I went anywhere. I didn't use it at home, because some of the doorways were not wide enough to accommodate it. I walked around the house by leaning on walls or grabbing onto furniture for support.

I fell a lot. I hit my head so hard in one fall, I "saw stars." I could not get up by myself when I fell. At times, I had to lay on the floor for hours and wait for someone to come home and help me. My daughters were terrified whenever they found me laying on the floor. My husband thought all the home monitoring systems were too expensive.

My husband deeply resented having to spend **"his"** money on my medical care. Our medical insurance reimbursed us for most of my medical expenses. My medical care cost us about
$500 a year.

My husband flew into a rage whenever we had to pay for anything for me. I broke my front tooth in a fall. His first comment was about how "f---ing" much it would cost us. It was less than $100. He told me that because of my medical bills we would not be able to afford to send our daughters to college.

My husband spent thousands of dollars a year on his toys (among them were a Porsche 911 and a Cessna 172 airplane). He felt entitled to do this. After all, he worked and I didn't. So, I did without necessities while his toy collection grew.

When it became difficult for me to write, I asked for an electric typewriter. My husband said "no." At the time, he had a computer, but he made it very clear to me that it was **"his"** computer and I was not to touch it. My parents bought me an electric typewriter. They also bought me a light-weight wheelchair because I could no longer walk long distances.

My husband expected rile to do the housework, laundry, cooking, etc. As I continued to lose strength in my arms, I could no longer carry a bag full of groceries or a basket of laundry. I had to rely on my daughters (who were then 7 and 8 years old) for help. My husband refused to get any household help even though my parents, and his mother, offered to pay for such help. He said that he did not trust anyone. He said that they would "rip us off."

The more my PLS progressed, the more cruel my husband became. In October 1988, I backed into a post and dented our car. My husband ordered me to stop driving. He said "I had no respect for property." From that day on, I became a virtual prisoner in my own home. I could not even go out in my own backyard, which overlooked the lake, because there were steps leading down to the patio and my husband refused to put in a ramp or even a handrail. My parents offered to pay for it.

I was made to feel very guilty for having PLS. I constantly heard how much my PLS inconvenienced my husband. He told me, in front of my daughters, that he hated me and he wished I were dead. Once, he threatened to kill me! I took this threat very seriously. I knew that he was capable of carrying it out. I was terrified to be home alone with my husband. (I am still haunted by the look of rage in his eyes. To this day, I cannot look at a picture of him).

I wanted to take my daughters and leave, but I felt I could not. I also felt I could not turn. my husband in for cruelty or abuse. My husband worked in the Law Enforcement field. He had the means to find me anywhere I went. I knew that he would take my daughters away from me when he found me. My husband told people that PLS was affecting my mind, thus making me an unfit mother, even though he knew that PLS does **not** affect the mind.

Sulphur Springs was the type of town where everyone knew everyone. My husband was a well-liked and respected member of the community. He projected an image of being a devoted husband. I felt it could cost me my life if I did anything to tarnish his reputation. So, I kept silent. My daughters and I were trapped in a "living hell" with no way out!

In 1989, my mother called the Muscular Dystrophy Association (MDA). They told her that PLS was a disease that they covered, since it is a variation of ALS. My mother made an appointment for me to be evaluated at an MDA clinic in Houston. I came to Houston in July 1989 for my evaluation. At the MDA clinic I met Dr. Stanley Appel, the head of the Neurology Department at

Baylor College of Medicine in Houston. He put me in the hospital for 2 days for "extensive testing."

I had so much blood drawn that I felt like I'd been attacked by a vampire. Many of the tests I'd had before: EEG, CT Scan, spinal tap. Among the "new" tests were a muscle biopsy (to definitively rule out ALS) and an EMG. To my knowledge, the EMG was the only test ever to have abnormal results. Based on the test results and my symptoms, Dr. Appel said definitively I did have primary lateral sclerosis.

In August 1989, my husband accepted a job in Austin. My daughters and I could not stay in our house while it was being sold, so we moved in with my parents in Houston. This was not an ideal situation, as I was used to living in my own home, but at least we were safe and I no longer had to live in fear for my life.

My parents opened their home to us. They made their house accessible for me. They helped me get adaptive equipment. They got me a raised toilet seat and put grab bars in the shower.

I enrolled my daughters (who were then 8 and 9 years old) in school. I started getting physical and occupational therapy 3 times a week at a facility about 5 miles from my parents' house.

I started receiving services from the Muscular Dystrophy Association. The first thing I received was a custom fit "hot pink" wheelchair. The wheelchair opened up a new world for me. MDA also got me a shower chair and a bedside toilet (I couldn't make it from my bedroom to the bathroom first thing in the morning).

My husband found an efficiency apartment in Austin. He came to Houston almost every weekend. On November 16, 1989 (while at work) my husband died of a ruptured aortic aneurysm. He was only 37 years old.

My husband's death came as a great shock to me. Despite the way he treated me, I never

stopped caring about him. I somehow managed to get through the next few months and handle all of the details and endless paperwork that had to be taken care of.

The shock of my husband's death and the memories of his abuse, on top of the physical limitations I have because of PLS were too much for me to handle. I went into a deep depression. I had no desire to go on living. I felt like a total failure as a mother because of my limitations. I thought my daughters would be better off without me. I felt that my daughters deserved a better mother. I felt that I was robbing my daughters of a "normal" happy childhood.

I was so deeply depressed and emotionally drained that I don't remember very much of what happened for about 6 years after my husband died. I did not take care of myself. I did not eat right, get enough rest, or do my stretching exercises regularly. I somehow functioned well enough to get by.

In early 1990, my sister dragged me into a psychologist's office. I received counseling for more than 7 years. The psychologist I saw, Dr. Avi Raphaeli, specializes in medical psychotherapy-the psychological effects of real medical conditions. Because PLS has left my speech unintelligible, I communicated with Dr. Raphaeli through a computer. I typed him a letter beforehand on my computer, and I used the computer keyboard in his office to communicate with him there.

It took me several months to open up to Dr. Raphaeli. I had been made to feel that I should be able to handle my problems myself, and that it was a sign of weakness to need help. My husband said counseling was a waste of money. He refused to get counseling because "no person with 2 good hands" could understand or help him.

Recovering from depression has been a long, difficult and painful process. I have had to overcome many obstacles. I have had many setbacks. I could not have come this far without counseling. Counseling has given me back the desire to function "to the best of my ability." I am doing better now emotionally than I have my whole life. I am getting back the desire and the energy to do everything I can in my battle against PLS.

My neurologist, Dr. Appel, prescribed an antidepressant (Elavil) to help control my depression and the inability to control emotions (uncontrollable and/or inappropriate crying and laughter) that both ALS and PLS cause. It took me a long time to "mentally" accept needing an antidepressant. Elavil has helped me to be calmer and on a more even keel. I don't want to go back to the way I was without it.

Dr. Raphaeli worked long and hard trying to convince me that I am not responsible for my husband's or anyone else's behavior, that I have **not** done anything wrong to feel guilty about, that it is **not** my fault I have PLS, and that my life has value and purpose. Thanks to his help I am slowly getting better. I no longer feel guilty about everything.

Dr. Raphaeli also helped me to be more assertive and to stand up and fight for my (and my daughters') rights. For the first time in years, I have some control of my life, and it feels good! Be assured, I will **never** let anyone else control my life again.

I am afraid that although the circumstances may be different, my story of abuse is all too common. Now that I have come to terms with the abuse I've suffered, I want to speak out in hopes of preventing someone else from going through the "living hell" I did!

No one should have to endure the degradations and indignities that I have. **EVERYONE,**
regardless of their disability, deserves to be loved and treated with dignity!

I urge anyone in an abusive situation to get out at the first sign of abuse. **Please** don't make the mistake I made and wait until it's too late. The abuse will only get worse, not better.

Don't make excuses or try to rationalize the abuser's behavior. There is **no** excuse or rationale for abuse ever!

Don't blame yourself for the abuser's behavior. You are **not** responsible for the abuser's or anyone else's behavior.

Don't think you can change the abuser's behavior-you can't! The abuser does **not** want to give up control over you.

Don't try to change yourself to please the abuser.

This **never** works. No matter how hard you try or how much you do, it is never enough and it's never done "well" enough.

Don't stay for the sake of the children. Children tend to mimic the behavior they grow up with. **Please** break the cycle of abuse. Get out **now,** so you can provide a warm, secure, loving environment for your children.

Don't let your fear of being on your own keep you from leaving. It is quite natural to be afraid. Recognize your fear, but, also remember that nothing you face "on the outside" will be as bad as what you've been through.

Don't keep silent about the abuse. One of my psychologist's favorite sayings is: "the best way to promote evil is to do nothing." The abuse will not stop if you don't take any action.

Please don't let the abuser coerce you into remaining silent. Please confide in someone and let them help you get out. You have nothing to be ashamed of. I put my own life and my daughters' lives in danger because I didn't speak out. I didn't let anyone know about my husband's abuse, nor did I allow anyone to help us.

I have a long way to go before I feel good about

myself. While I no longer feel totally useless and worthless, I have little self-esteem. This is primarily due to the effects and physical limitations PLS has caused. PLS has left me able to "do" very little.

I also feel PLS has made me physically unattractive. I don't like to look in a mirror. I feel my daughters are embarrassed by my appearance.

There are still many times that I feel like a failure as a mother. Dr. Raphaeli spent countless sessions telling me that all my children need from me is my unconditional love, which they have. It is hard for me not to feel guilty about not being able to "do" things for and with my children. The hardest part of having PLS (for me) is the burden it has placed on my daughters.

I could not have asked for 2 more wonderful children. I could not get through the day without their help. They help me dress, they fix me meals, and they do whatever I ask of them. Their love and support gives me the inner strength and determination I need to keep on fighting PLS. My psychologist assured me they were both healthy, well-adjusted teenagers. At times, I didn't think that I was going to survive my daughters' adolescences.

My daughters are now 20 & 21. One is a junior in

college. One is a senior in college. One wants to be a high school teacher. One wants to be a nurse. I am very proud of my daughters. They have not had easy lives They have always worked hard and made good grades. They both work part-time to pay for their college expenses. My daughters have chosen professions which we have a definite shortage. Teachers and nurses certainly deserve to be paid better than they are paid now.

I have been through a lot of changes in the past 10 years. In January 1990, I was dropped from the facility where I was getting physical & occupational therapy for "failure to progress." I was told if I did not show some improvement, my insurance would stop paying for my therapy. No one checked with my doctor, or my insurance carrier, before they decided to drop me from therapy.

I was shocked! I knew that I needed range-of-motion exercises regularly to keep my PLS from progressing rapidly. Neighbors of my parents, some of whom I'd never met before, volunteered to come over during the week and do these exercises.

In February 1990, a physical therapist who works with MDA evaluated me and developed a range-of-motion exercise program for me. She came to my parents' house and trained my family, and the group of volunteers, to do the exercises for my hands, arms and legs.

In 1990, I was evaluated by an occupational therapist who works with MDA. She gave me foam to go around my utensils and rubber grips to go on my pens & pencils. She signed me up for the "Books on Tape" program which is available, free of charge, to blind and physically disabled people. She also fitted me with a neck brace which supports my head when I'm typing, reading or watching TV.

I enjoy reading. Due to PLS, I am not able to turn pages in books or magazines. The MDA lent me an automatic page turner. I can keep it for as long as I am able to use it.

I was also evaluated by a speech therapist, who works with MDA, in 1990. She gave me an alphabet chart. At her suggestion, I got a small, hand-held Spell Check which I can type out words on.

In February 1992, I started getting physical & occupational therapy 3 times a week at Memorial Rehabilitation Hospital, which is about 5 miles from my house. In October 2000, they moved outpatient therapy to the Memorial Physical Therapy and Sports Rehabilitation center. It is about 2 miles from my house. I work with the same physical and occupational therapists who I worked with at Memorial Rehabilitation Hospital. My insurance carrier pays for it. They know the purpose of my therapy is to slow the rate of progression of my PLS. Dr. Appel feels therapy has helped slow the rate of progression of my PLS.

My physical and occupational therapists do range-of-motion exercises on my legs, arms and hands. My attendants do range-of-motion exercises on my legs, arms and hands on the days I do not go to therapy.

I work on "grasp and release" activities to strengthen my arms and hands in occupational therapy. I also paint stained glass pictures with my right hand in occupational therapy. I put my right and in an elevating mobile arm support. (Painting satisfies my creative urge). I can walk more than 800 feet using a (Rifton) walker with wheels, and trunk and arm supports in physical therapy.

I jokingly say that I am convinced "PT" stands for "Patient Torture." My therapists have become my friends. They have been very supportive. They have not let me give up on myself.

I now know what a difference feeling loved and supported can make. My entire family has been supportive. My parents and my brothers and sisters are always there to lend a helping hand or give a word of encouragement.

I am living proof of the adage that "life begins at 40." Within a few months after I turned 40, in June 1993, I got an electric wheelchair, a laptop computer & a voice synthesizer, and I bought a two-story townhouse (about a mile from my parents' house).

The first floor of the townhouse is wheelchair accessible. I can get around by myself. I had ramps poured at the front & back doors, a roll-in shower put in the bathroom, and an adjustable height desk built in my bedroom for my desk top computer. In some ways, it is a blessing to have my daughters' rooms upstairs. I don't have to see the mess in their rooms every day.

In 1993, a speech therapist, who works with the Muscular Dystrophy Association, helped me find an augmentative communication system that best suited my needs. I bought an augmentative communication system that had an IBM compatible laptop computer and a Multi-Voice voice synthesizer, which had 9 voices. The software programs are from Words Plus. It had EZ Keys which features include: word prediction, abbreviations and automatic word endings. I could access key phrases in just a few keystrokes. It also had Scanning WSKE which can be accessed by a variety of switches. I could use it when I was unable to type on a keyboard.

In July 1999, the Texas Rehabilitation Commission bought me a new augmentative communication system: a new IBM compatible laptop computer, a new voice synthesizer (which has 9 voices) and updated Words+ software. My old voice synthesizer no longer worked and my old laptop computer barely worked. My old Words+ software program ran in DOS. My new Words+ software program runs in Windows. I had never used Windows or a mouse.

My daughters, who have been using computers since they were in kindergarten, showed me how to use Windows. I know how to do almost everything in Windows that I did in DOS. I know how to send a letter I have typed by E-mail, how to forward E-mails and how to look up specific websites on the Internet. I am still learning how to "surf the Internet."

I can move the mouse on my new laptop computer with my right thumb. I can also type on my new laptop computer and move the mouse using a switch (a small round disc) which I put on a velcro strap. I put the strap around my left leg. I touch the switch with my hand.

My new laptop computer has an environmental control unit. I can turn a lamp on-and-off, and change channels on my television through my laptop computer. I can also hook-up a microphone to my laptop computer and to talk to people, on the phone, using my voice synthesizer.

In 1996, I bought a 1991 Chevrolet van, with about 90,000 miles on it. I had a wheelchair lift installed in it. I spent about $4000 to keep it running. I sold my Chevrolet van to an ALS family in the Houston area, in June 2000. Their son works on cars a lot. He should be able to keep it running for a few more years. It had 117,000 miles on it when I sold it.
In June 2000, I bought a 1993 Dodge mini-van, with only about 30,000 miles on it. (My parents helped pay for it). It is in excellent condition. It has a dropped floor. The wheelchair straps into the front passenger seat. It has a remote control that opens up the side door on the van and lowers the ramp.

I saw an ad for the mini-van in the ALS Digest (an ALS newsletter that is distributed by E- mail, by a man in Florida, to more than 4000 people in the US and 60 countries). Ironically, the mini-van belonged to a woman I knew from the Houston ALS Support Group (Sharon Sell). Sharon died in September 1999.

I feel fairly comfortable with my daughters driving my Dodge mini-van. I didn't feel very comfortable with them driving my Chevrolet (full size) van. Having a van that I can ride in, in my wheelchair, makes it easier for my daughters and my attendants to take me places: therapy, my doctors' offices, movies and shopping. It is a "hassle" to put me into a car and fold-up my wheelchair so it will fit in the trunk or the back seat.

I have had several attendants over the past 8 years. All of my attendants have cared about me and they have all taken good care of me. Before my daughters had their driver's licenses, I had a "live-in" attendant during the week. I have an attendant during the day, while my daughters go to school and work. My daughters take care of me at night and on weekends.

Having PLS has taught me to value life and get my priorities straight. My faith has been strengthened. I have met some truly wonderful people. I now realize that there really are people who care about me, regardless of my disability.

It has also forced me to use a computer. For several months after my husband's death, I could not even enter the room "his" computer was in without getting queazy. It took over a year for me to be able to use "his" computer. I comfortably used it for about 5 years, until it became obsolete.

Another positive thing is that PLS is one of the 40+ neuromuscular diseases covered by the Muscular Dystrophy Association. I am very grateful for all they have done for me, at no cost to me. I see Dr. Appel every 6-8 months in the Vicki Appel MDA/ALS Neuromuscular Clinic. Dr. Appel is hopeful that researchers will find a cure for ALS in the next few years. He said that people with PLS will benefit from the findings of ALS research since PLS is a variation of ALS.

MDA and the ALS Association sponsor local ALS Support Groups where people with ALS can come together and share ideas, feelings and thoughts with each other. MDA sponsors the Houston ALS Support Group. We often have speakers who work in the field of neuromuscular disease, at the meetings. One tip from a physical therapist I have found to be very helpful is: to spend your time and energy on what is important to you and to let the unimportant stuff go.

At a few meetings, we have had doctors who do research on ALS speak to us about the status of ALS research. They talked about possible causes. They explained the varying drug studies. I am excited about the recent progress that has been made in ALS research. I believe a cure is on the horizon, and that hope of a cure sustains me through the hard times.

The people in the Houston ALS Support Group are wonderful. The courageous manner in which they are facing and fighting ALS, which is much worse than PLS, touches me deeply. They are an inspiration to me. They have enriched my life.

I was hesitant to become involved with the Houston ALS Support Group because of the fatal nature of ALS. I did not know if I was emotionally strong enough to handle it.

In February 1994, a truly beautiful person (Betty Porter) lost her valiant battle with ALS. Betty enriched the lives of everyone who was fortunate enough to know her. She always had a smile which would light up an entire room.

Betty and I shared a special bond, as we both had voice synthesizers. I felt honored when Betty shared her story with me. I was very moved by it. I will always treasure it. I feel very blessed to have known Betty. She was a fighter to the end. Her death had a profound impact on me. It was the first time I had to face the loss of a friend due to ALS.

The "unfairness" of ALS robbing such a special person of life makes me very angry and frustrated. I know that Heaven has been graced by Betty's presence. I feel that with her prayers from above a cure, or an effective treatment, for ALS will soon be found.

The cure can't come soon enough! Sadly, people like Betty are dying every day from ALS. In the past 7 years, ALS has taken the lives of several friends from the Houston ALS Support Group.

ALS is a cruel disease. It attacks a healthy body and literally sucks the life out of it, while leaving the mind intact. I **DO NOT** want to lose any more friends to ALS. It has to be stopped **now!**

Few people have ever heard of PLS. Frank Levy, Ph.D has done extensive research on PLS. He probably knows as much as anyone does about PLS. Dr. Levy is very willing to share his knowledge of PLS with others. I have asked him numerous questions. He has always done his best to answer them.

Few PLS people know about the PLS Support Group & Newsletter. My sister obtained Dr. Levy's name and address for me from the ALS Association. Currently there are about 600 PLS people on the PLS Newsletter's mailing list. To my knowledge, there is only one other PLS person, in the Houston area, on it. I know about one man and one woman, in the Houston area, who have been diagnosed with PLS. I know there are probably more than 3 people, in the Houston area, who have PLS.

I encourage anyone with PLS to contact Dr. Frank Levy and to subscribe to the PLS Newsletter. Subscriptions are $7.50 a year. The address is: PLS Newsletter/ Frank Levy, PhD, Editor/ 101 Pinta Court/ Los Gatos, CA 95032. If you wish a written response from Dr. Levy please include a self-addressed, stamped envelope. You can reach Dr. Levy by phone 408-356-8227 (aftenoons only). Dr. Levy's E-mail address is: 73112.611@compuserve.com [Please note this information was last updated in 2000]

I also encourage anyone with PLS to contact their local MDA chapter or the ALS Association to find an ALS Support Group in their area. I have received a lot of helpful information from the ALS Association and the newsletter they publish.

I am continuing to "hold my own" in my battle with PLS. The strength in my shoulders, arms, and hands is poor. I cannot lift my arms more than a few inches, without support. My leg strength and balance are fair.

PLS has left me unable to close my lips. It has also affected my tongue. This makes eating very difficult. I can only eat soft & pureed foods. I have trouble holding saliva in my mouth. I often drool. It embarrasses me and I know it embarrasses my daughters when I drool- in public.

- I take more than 30 pills a day. I take all of my pills in soft foods like oatmeal, applesauce, pudding or jello. I take assorted vitamins and supplements. I know that they have helped me. Dr. Appel recommended I take antioxidant vitamins (Vitamin C, Vitamin E & Beta Carotene). I found out about two of the supplements (Evening Primrose Oil & CoQ10) through friends. I found out about two of the supplements (Lecithin and C-3036) through the PLS Newsletter.

I had a feeding tube put in my stomach in January 1995 because I can't swallow liquids. I choke on them or they go down my airway. It took my doctor several months to "talk me into" getting a feeding tube. I knew I was not getting enough liquid in my body. I knew I needed a feeding tube, but the thought of putting a scope down my throat to my stomach, while I was awake, terrified me. When the opportunity arose for me to have a feeding tube put in during surgery to take out my gallbladder, I took it. I had surgery at the hospital closest to my house, Memorial City Hospital. I developed a lot of post-operative problems. It took me about 5 months to recover from them.

Dr. Appel, my neurologist referred me to a gastroenterologist, Dr. John McKechnie. Dr. McKechnie said the hole in my stomach would start to close immediately if the feeding tube was not in it. He said if the hole closed too much, he would have to put a scope down my throat to my stomach to reopen the hole.

Dr. McKechnie said if I couldn't get the feeding tube

back in the hole in my stomach, to go to the nearest hospital to have it replaced. I have had to have my feeding tube replaced 8 times, and only 2 times were planned. My feeding tube has fallen out of my stomach 6 times.

Once, my feeding tube fell out on a Saturday night. My daughters could not get the feeding tube to stay in the hole in my stomach, so they took me to a hospital about 3 miles from our house. We had the pleasure of spending 4 hours in the Emergency Room at Memorial City Hospital. The ER doctor could not get my feeding tube back in the hole. He could not find another feeding tube, so he used catheter tubing to keep the hole in my stomach open. The ER doctor told me to see my gastroenterologist as soon as possible, so I could get a new feeding tube. I had the pleasure of spending 3 hours Monday morning at the Methodist Hospital where Dr. McKechnie works, to get a new feeding tube.

Twice, my attendants have been able to get my feeding tube back in the hole. They taped it to my stomach well enough to last for the trip to Dr. McKechnie's office. My former attendant (who is staying home with her baby she had in October 2000) and my youngest daughter have been able to replace my feeding tube the past 2 times it has fallen out. (My oldest daughter doesn't think she would be able to replace my feeding tube). I try to always have a spare feeding tube. I am never sure when my feeding tube will fall out.

In August 1995, I was diagnosed with Crohn's disease, an inflammatory bowel disease. Medication is controlling the severe abdominal pain and rectal bleeding I was experiencing. My gastroenterologist and my neurologist feel that Crohn's disease is not related to PLS.

The most frustrating part of PLS (for me) is that my speech is unintelligible. My daughters can still understand some of what I say. I have to spell-out most of what I want to say to them. This is often very frustrating for them. I have to communicate with my doctors and therapists by letter. Typing is difficult as PLS has left me with very little use of my hands. As time consuming as it is, I am grateful to have the ability to communicate.

I think that the combination of: counseling, therapy, medication, vitamins and supplements has benefitted me greatly. I feel better (physically and emotionally) than I've felt in a long, long time.

I feel that I have finally overcome depression. Thanks to counseling, I'm finally able to put the past "in the past." I've learned not to spend my (valuable) energy dwelling on the past because nothing can change it.

I now try to focus my energy on the present and what's really important: being the best mother I can be to my daughters, speaking out about the abuse I have suffered in hopes of stopping abusive treatment of the disabled, and doing whatever I can to help in the efforts to find a cure for ALS and PLS.

I have never considered primary lateral sclerosis to be a death sentence. I will never give up hope for a cure. I try to maintain a positive attitude and a sense of humor. I take life one day at a time.

I am grateful for each new day. I try to always be mindful of the many blessings God has given me: 2 beautiful daughters, a loving and supportive family, caring friends and attendants, and wonderful doctors and therapists.

I don't know what the future holds for me, but I know that my faith and the love and support of my family and friends will get me through it. I have just begun to put my life together and I **am not** about to let PLS, or anything else, stop me now!

I know now that my life has value and purpose. Everyone's life does. I know now that life is worth living, despite the seemingly insurmountable problems and obstacles that we all have in our lives. I know that I am a stronger person because of everything I have been through. If my story helps even one person, it will be worth all the time and effort I put into writing it.

In Loving Memory – Entry by Beth's youngest daughter

On Monday, October 20, 2008, at the age of 55, Beth unexpectedly went to join our Lord after a brief battle with pneumonia following a fall and hip fracture. Her body was generously donated to ALS research as would have been her wishes. Beth's daughters are both nearing the age Beth was when she started writing her story. Neither have any symptoms of Primary Lateral Sclerosis. Both of Beth's daughters were married and pregnant with their first children at the time of her passing. They find closure and joy knowing that their mother is free of the constraints of her body and is watching over them and their families with a smile on her face.

Beth's oldest daughter found her mother's passion in becoming a special education teacher as well as a youth minister. She is now a mother of three. Beth's youngest daughter became a nursing as well as a nurse educator. She is the mother of two, one of whom faces his own medical challenges with a faith that echoes his grandmother's.

In the years since Beth's passing, her daughters have grown inseparably close. They often imagine the smile that would light Beth's face if she could see her five grandchildren laughing and playing together. Those moments—real or imagined—are reminders that her spirit is never far away. Beth's legacy is etched not only in their memories, but in their lives of service, compassion, and resilience. Beth will forever be remembered as a kind and gentle soul, who despite her illness, had the most gracious smile.

"May her strength remind us to stand, her smile remind us to find the joy in the midst of obstacles, and her life remind us to never give up."

Made in the USA
Coppell, TX
26 August 2025